Find and circle 8 objects that begin with the letter **a** in this Hidden Pictures® puzzle.

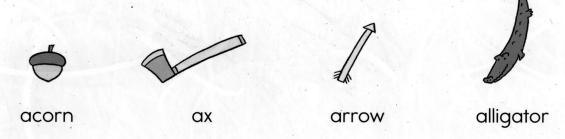

acorn   ax   arrow   alligator

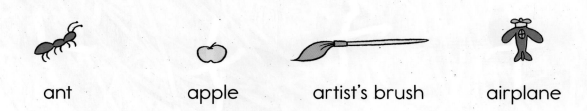

ant   apple   artist's brush   airplane

Trace the letters to write a sentence about the big picture.

Alan and the apes
always amaze the
audience.

Bella Badger's Bonnet

Circle each B you see. How many did you find?

BARBARA'S BONNETS

OPEN

4

Answers on page 52

Hunt for letters as you read this poem.
Circle each **B** you see. Draw a box around each **b** you see.

Bella Badger rode her bike
To buy herself a bonnet.
But how did Bella choose her hat?
It had a **B** upon it!

Poem by Jody Jensen Shaffer

Trace the letters to write a silly sentence.

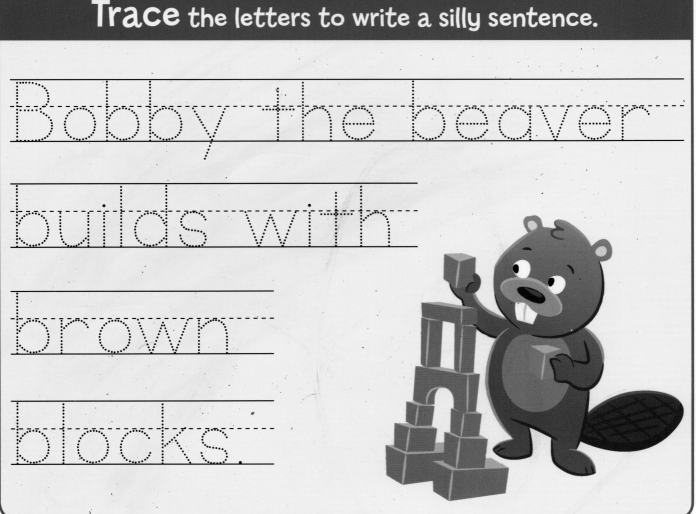

Bobby the beaver
builds with
brown
blocks.

Art by Katie McDee

Answers on page 52

C Is For?

How many things can you find that begin with the letter c?

Art by Dave Klug

Answers on page 52

Trace the letters to write some words that start with c.
Can you find these things in the big picture?

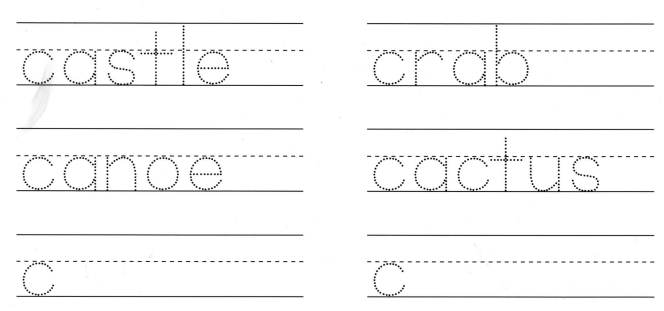

castle

crab

canoe

cactus

c

c

Follow the steps to draw a cat.

1.

2.

3.

4.

Dog Search

Can you find 10 dogs in this scene?

Answers on page 52

Write some animal names that begin with the letter d.

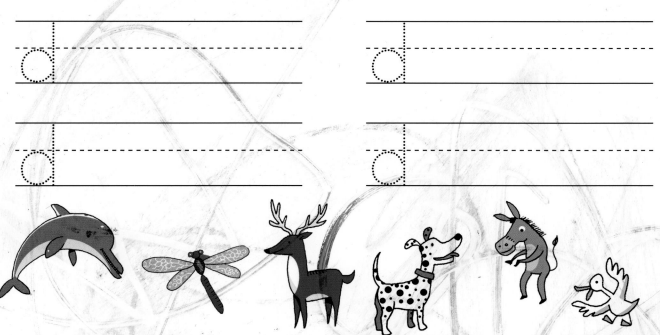

D_____   D_____

D_____   D_____

Draw a line between each matching pair of dragons.

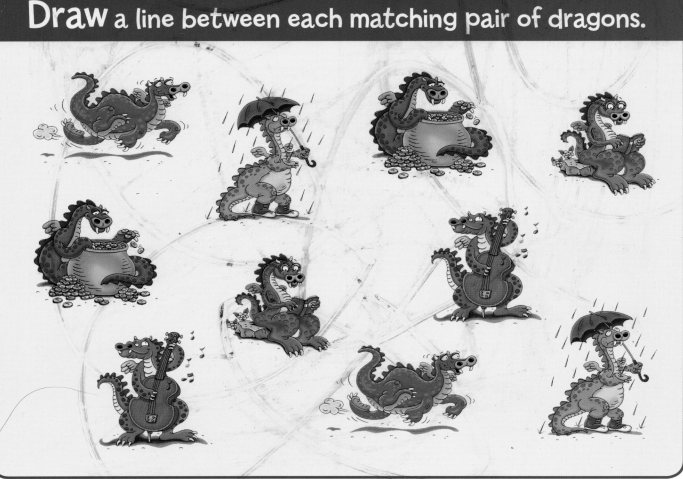

Art by Dave Klug

Art by Paul Montgomery

Answers on page 52

Eggs for Everyone

Art by Kelly Kennedy

Find and circle 8 objects that begin with the letter e in this Hidden Pictures® puzzle.

eraser   envelope   emerald   elephant

eyeglasses   eel   eagle   easel

Trace the letters to write a sentence about the big picture.

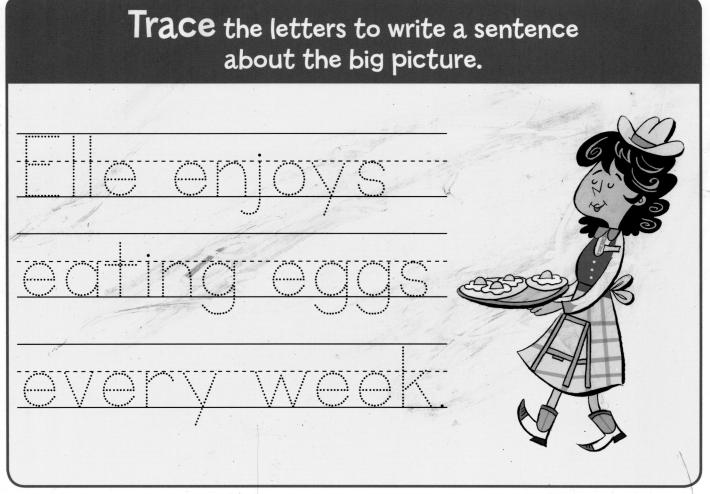

Elle enjoys eating eggs every week.

The Fly and the Frog

Circle each F you see. How many did you find?

Answers on page 52

Hunt for letters as you read this poem.
Circle each **F** you see. Draw a box around each **f** you see.

Felix the fly flew right past her,

But Felicity's tongue was much faster.

Fortunately for Felicity,

Felix wasn't a bee.

A stung tongue would have been a disaster.

Trace the letters to write a silly sentence.

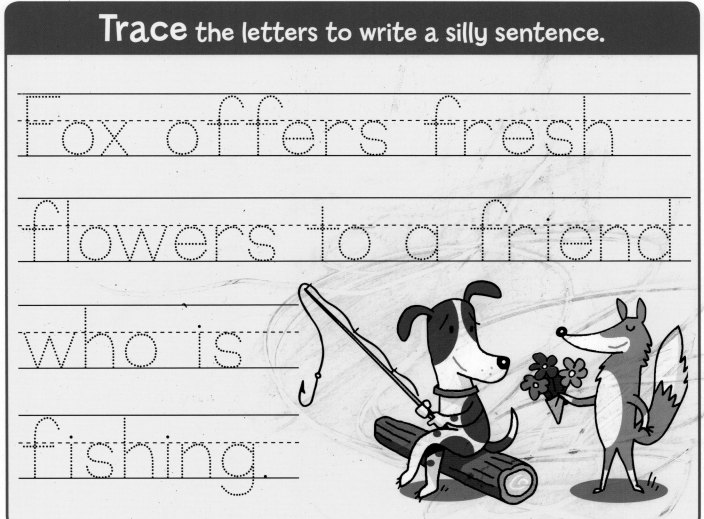

Fox offers fresh

flowers to a friend

who is

fishing.

Answers on page 52

G Is For?

How many things can you find that begin with the letter g?

Answers on page 53

Trace the letters to write some words that start with g.
Can you find these things in the big picture?

giraffe

guitar

gorilla

grapes

g

g

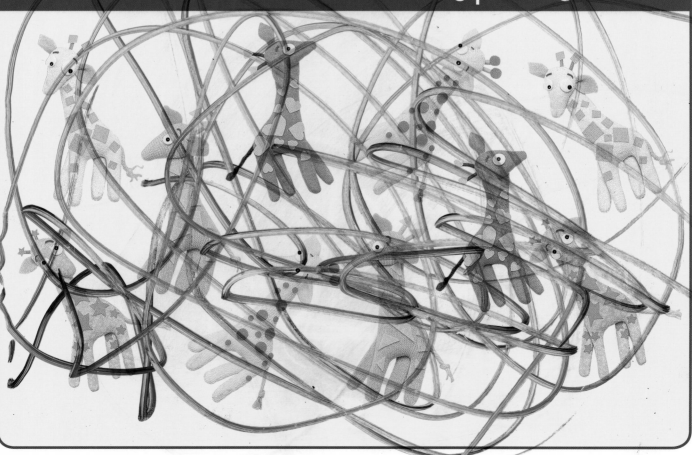

Draw a line between each matching pair of giraffes.

Art by Carol Baicker Mc-Kee

Hannah's Hairbrush

Find and circle 8 objects that begin with the letter h in this Hidden Pictures® puzzle.

heart · horn · hamburger · hockey stick

hot dog · handbag · hammer · horseshoe

Trace the letters to write a sentence about the big picture.

Hannah and her

mom brush

hair together

I Scream for Ice Cream

Circle each I you see. How many did you find?

Answers on page 53

Art by Mick Reid

Hunt for letters as you read this poem.
Circle each I you see. Draw a box around each i you see.

My ice-cream cone is leaking

and dribbling down my chin.

It draws a beard and mustache

and paints a chocolate grin!

Poem by Carol McAdoo Rehme

Trace the letters to write a tongue twister.
Then say it five times, fast.

I see icy

iguanas

ice-skating.

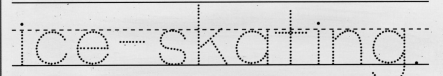

Art by Valeri Gorbachev

Answers on page 53

Juggling Jesters

Find and circle 8 objects that begin with the letter j in this Hidden Pictures® puzzle.

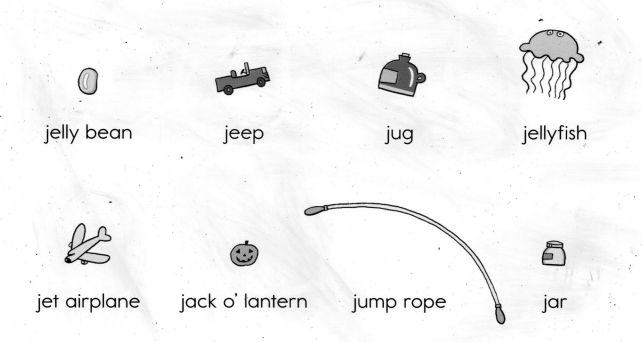

jelly bean   jeep   jug   jellyfish

jet airplane   jack o' lantern   jump rope   jar

Trace the letters to write a sentence about the big picture.

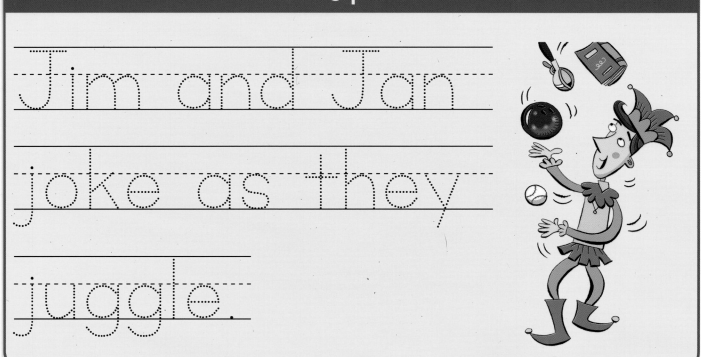

Jim and Jan joke as they juggle.

Answers on page 53

Key Search

Can you find 10 keys in this scene?

Answers on page 53

Trace the letters to write a silly sentence with the letter k.

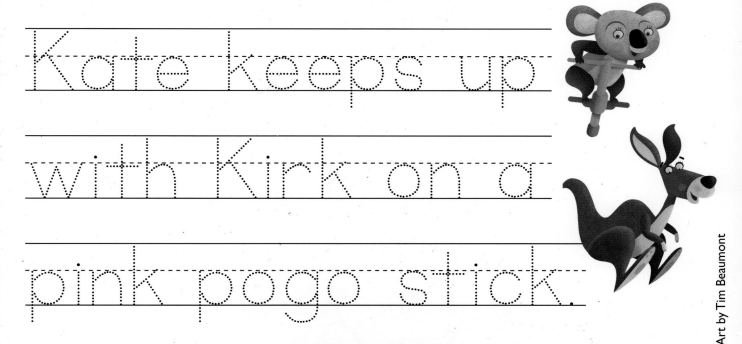

Kate keeps up
with Kirk on a
pink pogo stick.

Art by Tim Beaumont

Follow the steps to draw a koala.

1.

2.

3.

4.

Lizards, Lizards, Lizards

Circle each **L** you see. How many did you find?

Art by Richard Johnson

Answers on page 53

Hunt for letters as you read this poem.
Circle each **L** you see. Draw a box around each **I** you see.

When lizards hatch from
Eggs, eggs, eggs,
They scurry about on their
Legs, legs, legs.
They climb on rocks where they
Run, run, run,
Then rest awhile in the
Sun, sun, sun.

Poem by Marguerite Chase McCue

Trace the letters to write a silly sentence.

Lionel the
lion likes
lemonade.

Art by Mike Dammer

M Is For?

How many things can you find that begin with the letter **m**?

Answers on page 54

Trace the letters to write some words that start with m. Can you find these things in the big picture?

music

magnet

mailbox

mom

m

m

Draw a line between each matching pair of monkeys.

Answers on page 54

New Neighbors

Art by Kelly Kennedy

Place these stickers to rate your favorite puzzles.

Find and circle 8 objects that begin with the letter n in this Hidden Pictures® puzzle.

necklace

necktie

nail

noodle

newt

notebook

nut

needle

Trace the letters to write a sentence about the big picture.

Nancy notices

her new

neighbors.

Otto's Garage

Circle each **O** you see. How many did you find?

Art by Lynne Cravath

Answers on page 54

Hunt for letters as you read this poem.
Circle each O you see. Draw a box around each o you see.

Hello, Otto,

My car is slow.

Flat tire? Oh, no!

Well, now I know

Why cars won't GO

Without an O.

Trace the letters to write a silly sentence.

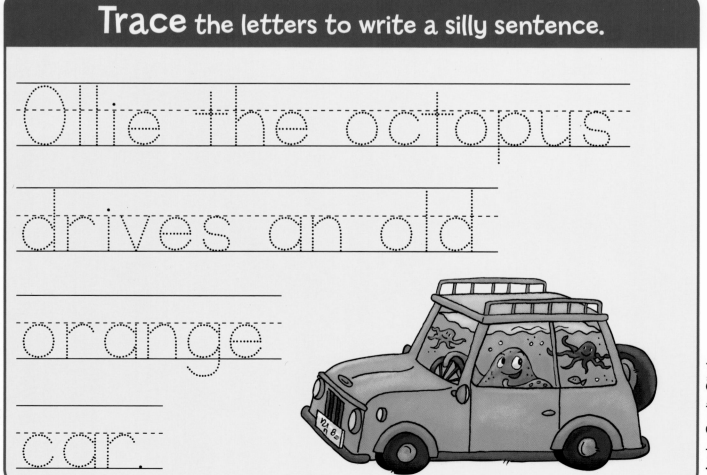

Ollie the octopus
drives an old
orange
car.

Penguin Power

Find and circle 8 objects that begin with the letter p in this Hidden Pictures® puzzle.

pickle   potato   pail   pie

pear   pencil   plane   paper clip

Trace the letters to write a sentence about the big picture.

Phillip is proud of his pals.

Quinn's Quilt

Circle each **Q** you see. How many did you find?

Answers on page 54

Hunt for letters as you read this sentence.
Circle each **Q** you see. Draw a box around each **q** you see.

Queen Jacqueline
quietly sews
her quilt.

Art by Kelly Kennedy

Trace the letters to write a silly sentence.

Quentin quickly

won the

quiz.

Art by David Helton

R Is For?

How many things can you find that begin with the letter r?

Art by Dave Klug

Answers on page 54

Trace the letters to write some words that start with **r**. Can you find these things in the big picture?

rainbow

rabbit

rocket

ruler

r

r

Follow the steps to draw a rocket.

1.

2.

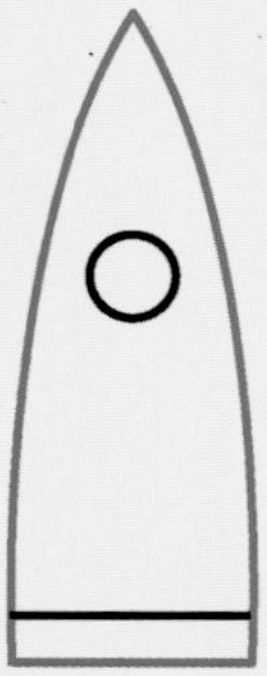

3.

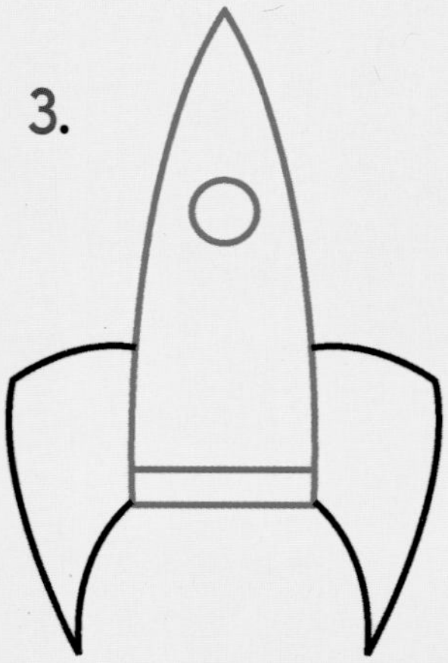

4.

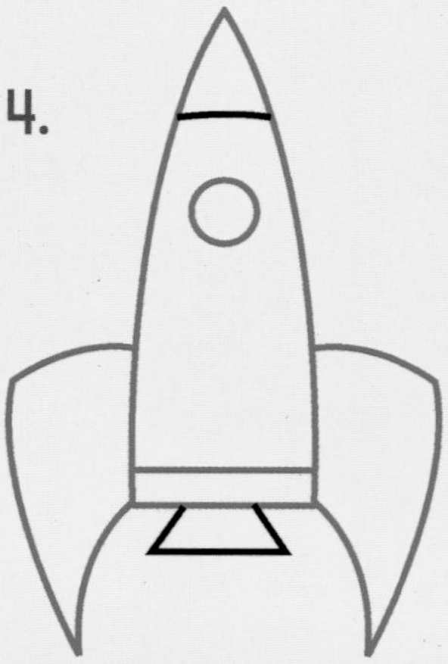

Super Sandwich

Art by Bob Ostrom

Find and circle 8 objects that begin with the letter s in this Hidden Pictures® puzzle.

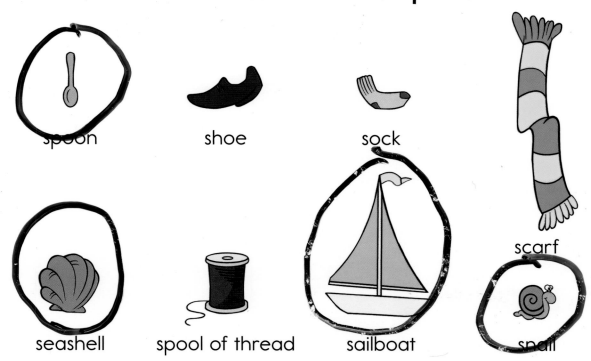

spoon

shoe

sock

scarf

seashell

spool of thread

sailboat

snail

Trace the letters to write a sentence about the big picture.

Sam slips extra

cheese on his

sandwich.

T-T-Transportation

Circle each **T** you see. How many did you find?

40

Answers on page 55

Hunt for letters as you read this poem.
Circle each T you see. Draw a box around each t you see.

Truck driver,
Tractor driver,
Train driver, too.

Honk! Honk!
Rrrr! Rrrr!
Woo-woo-woooo!

Poem by John Madian

Trace the letters to write a silly sentence.

Two tigers
in tights
walked on
a tightrope.

Art by John Bendall-Brunello

Answers on page 55

Umbrella Search

Can you find 10 umbrellas in this scene?

Answers on page 55

Trace the letters to write a silly sentence with the letter u.

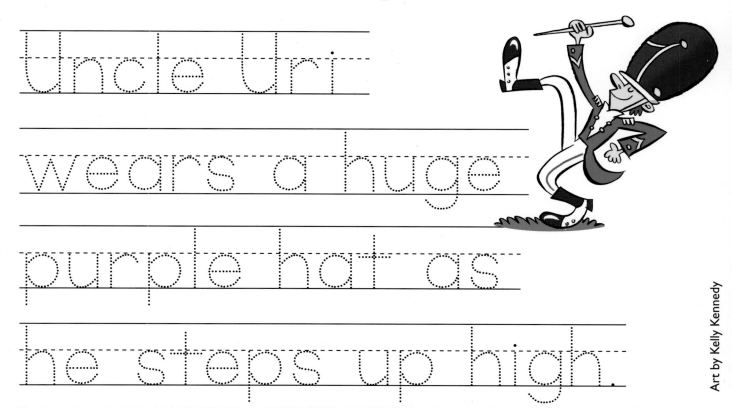

Uncle Uri
wears a huge
purple hat as
he steps up high.

Art by Kelly Kennedy

Follow the steps to draw a unicorn.

1.

2.

3.

4.

43

A Visit to the Vet

Art by Kelly Kennedy

Find and circle 8 objects that begin with the letter v in this Hidden Pictures® puzzle.

valentine

van

vest

violin

volcano

vase

visor

volleyball

Trace the letters to write a sentence about the big picture.

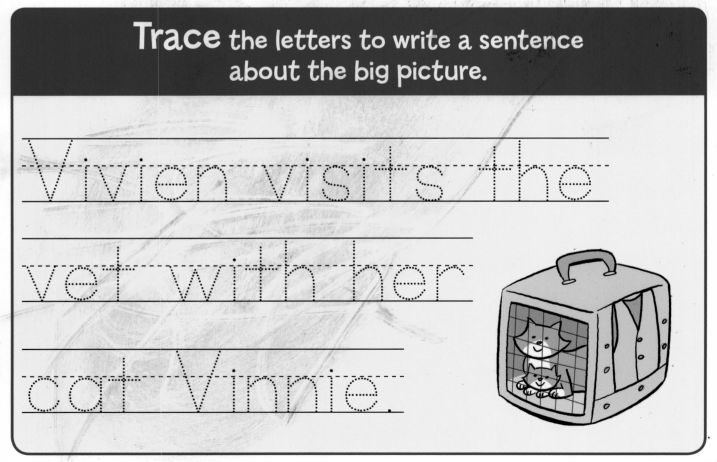

Vivien visits the vet with her cat Vinnie.

Answers on page 55

W Is For?

How many things can you find that begin with the letter w?

Answers on page 55

Trace the letters to write some words that start with **w**. Can you find these things in the big picture?

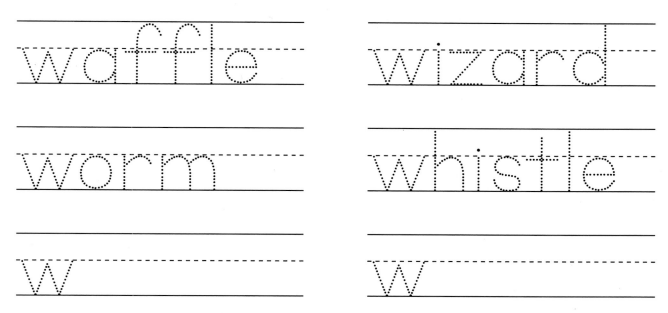

waffle

worm

w

wizard

whistle

w

Follow the steps to draw a walrus.

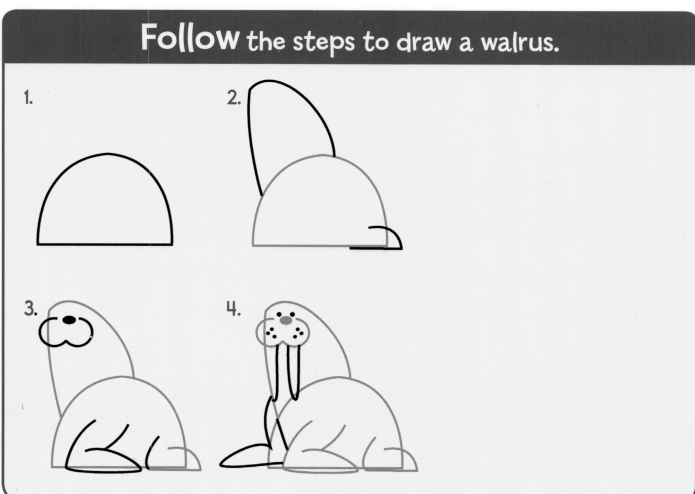

1.

2.

3.

4.

Answers on page 55

X Marks the Spot

Hunt for letters as you read this sentence.
Circle each **X** you see. Draw a box around each **x** you see.

Xavier can't relax
until he spells
xylophone.

Trace the letters to write a silly sentence.

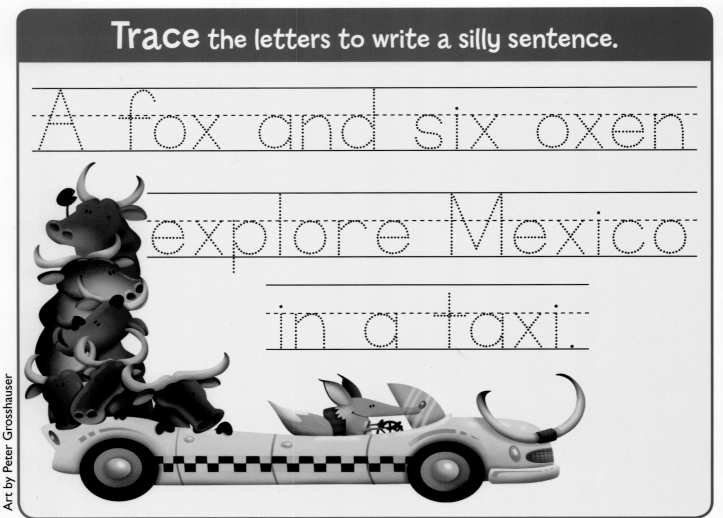

A fox and six oxen
explore Mexico
in a taxi.

Art by Kelly Kennedy

Art by Peter Grosshauser

Answers on page 55

Y Not?

Hunt for letters as you read this sentence.
Circle each **Y** you see. Draw a box around each **y** you see.

Yolanda wonders
if she should use
only sunny yellow.

Art by Kelly Kennedy

Trace the letters to write a tongue twister.
Then say it five times, fast.

Yellow yaks wear
speckled
slacks.

Art by Kevin Zimmer

Answers on page 55

Zippy Zs

Hunt for letters as you read this sentence. Circle each **Z** you see. Draw a box around each **z** you see.

Zack breezes through his zebra door.

ZEBRA

Trace the letters to write some words with **z** in them.

buzz

puzzle

jazz

zebra

pizza

Answers on page 55

Write the Alphabet!

Answers

PAGE 2 Awesome Acrobats

PAGE 4 Bella Badger's Bonnet

PAGE 5 Hunt for Letters

Bella **B**adger rode her **b**ike
To **b**uy herself a **b**onnet.
But how did **B**ella choose her hat?
It had a **B** upon it!

PAGE 6 C Is For?

Here are the **c** words we found. You may
have found others.

1. cactus
2. cage
3. camel
4. camera
5. canary
6. canoe
7. cap
8. carrots
9. castle
10. caterpillar
11. cattails
12. city
13. climber
14. cloud
15. clown
16. coin
17. corn
18. couch
19. crab
20. cracker
21. crane
22. crayons
23. creek
24. crib
25. crown

PAGE 8 Dog Search

PAGE 9 Matching

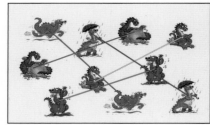

PAGE 10 Eggs for Everyone

PAGE 12 The Fly and the Frog

PAGE 13 Hunt for Letters

Felix the **f**ly **f**lew right past her,
But **F**elicity's tongue
was much **f**aster.
Fortunately for **F**elicity,
Felix wasn't a bee.
A stung tongue would
have been a disaster.

Answers

PAGE 14 G Is For?

Here are the **g** words we found. You may have found others.

1. game	11. goldfish
2. garage	12. Goldilocks
3. garbage can	13. golf ball
4. garbage truck	14. gorilla
5. garden	15. grapefruit
6. gate	16. grapes
7. gift	17. grass
8. giraffe	18. green beans
9. glasses	19. groundhog
10. goat	20. guitar

PAGE 15 Matching

PAGE 16 Hannah's Hairbrush

PAGE 18 I Scream for Ice Cream

PAGE 19 Hunt for Letters

My ice-cream cone is leaking
and dribbling down my chin.
It draws a beard and mustache
and paints a chocolate grin!

PAGE 20 Juggling Jesters

PAGE 22 Key Search

PAGE 24 Lizards, Lizards, Lizards

PAGE 25 Hunt for Letters

When lizards hatch from
Eggs, eggs, eggs,
They scurry about on their
Legs, legs, legs.
They climb on rocks where they
Run, run, run,
Then rest awhile in the
Sun, sun, sun.

Answers

PAGE 26 M Is For?

Here are the **m** words we found. You may have found others.

1. magazine
2. magnet
3. mail
4. mailbox
5. mailman
6. man
7. manhole
8. maple leaf
9. meter
10. microphone
11. microscope
12. minivan
13. mirror
14. mom
15. money
16. moose
17. mouse
18. museum
19. music
20. mustache

PAGE 27 Matching

PAGE 28 New Neighbors

PAGE 30 Otto's Garage

PAGE 31 Hunt for Letters

Hell**o** **O**tto,

My car is sl**o**w.

Flat tire? **O**h, n**o**!

Well, n**o**w I kn**o**w

Why cars w**o**n't G**O**

With**o**ut an **O**.

PAGE 32 Penguin Power

PAGE 34 Quinn's Quilt

PAGE 35 Hunt for Letters

Queen Jac**q**ueline
quietly sews
her **q**uilt.

PAGE 36 R Is For?

Here are the **r** words we found. You may have found others.

1. rabbit
2. race car
3. raft
4. railroad
5. rainbow
6. raincoat
7. raisins
8. rake
9. rat
10. rattlesnake
11. reindeer
12. rhino
13. rice
14. robin
15. rock
16. rocket
17. roller skates
18. rope
19. ruler
20. runner